THIS SCARY-COOL ANNUAL BELONGS TO

....

This edition published by Parragon Books Ltd in 2015
Parragon Books Ltd
Chartist House
15–17 Trim Street
Bath BA1 1HA, UK
www.parragon.com

ISBN 978-1-4748-0936-8

Printed in Poland

CONTENTS

WELCOME!

GRUB'S UP
Take a look at our brand new outdoor Creepateria on page 16. There's even a new menu to suit the health-conscious undead.

Hey, **GHOULFRIENDS!** It's Frankie Stein here – in this year's Annual we're giving you a sneaky look at our **FANGTASTIC FEARBOOK!** We've had a totally **CLAWSOME** year here at **MONSTER HIGH**, full of freaky-fab **GROANING-ONS** and tons of **SCARY-COOL** excitement. Relive the glories of the **FEAR SQUAD**, check out the **ROARSOME ROMANCES** and, of course, get to know your **FAVOURITE GHOULFRIENDS** better! All this plus lots of **MONSTERIFIC ACTIVITIES** to do at home. Finish off by filling your **FEARBOOK** with autographs from all your beast friends. Stay **PERFECTLY IMPERFECT!**

Frankie
Stein
xxx

MONSTER HIGH

HAVE SCHOOL SPIRIT

Frankie Stein™

I'm newly stitched together – how many days has it been now? **BEING A GHOUL AT MONSTER HIGH** makes my bolts spark and I'm all about showing **SCREAM SPIRIT.** I'm a member of the Fear Squad but I'm still a bit clumsy.... Sometimes **I GET SO ENTHUSIASTIC** when I'm cheering that my stitches come loose and one of my limbs flies off – how **MORTALFYING** is that?!! But my scary-cool ghoulfriends still love me, especially my GFFS Draculaura and Clawdeen. **MONSTER HIGH RULES!**

"Stitched together with style"

MONSTER HIGH

HAVE KILLER STYLE

Clawdeen Wolf™

From the tips of my **BLING-RINGED EARS** to the ends of my paw-fectly manicured claws, I always make sure that I look **FUR-ROCIOUSLY FABULOUS**. I am a fierce **FASHIONISTA** and I change my hairstyle as often as I change my **SKY-HIGH WEDGE TRAINERS**! I'm proud of my intense golden eyes and my gore-geous mane of auburn hair, not to mention my **SUPER-CUTE CANINES**! I love being part of a **WEREWOLF** pack ... except when my little sis' Howleen steals my clothes. No one messes with **MY FREAKY-FAB STYLE**!

"Some monsters say I've got an eye for fashion and I have to admit they're right"

WHAT'S IN MY BAG?
A hairbrush to keep my mane looking fangtastic!

MONSTER HIGH

THROW A KILLER PARTY!

Cleo de Nile™

Hey, remember the totally **FANGTASTIC BANQUET** that I put on for Frightday the 13th? It was totally **MAJESTIC!** That's hardly a surprise, though – **I AM AN ANCIENT EGYPTIAN PRINCESS!** With the help of my personal assistant – I mean, GFF – Ghoulia Yelps and **MY FAVOURITE MANSTER** Deuce Gorgon™, I rule the school and don't take no for an answer. Well, I am **MONSTER ROYALTY**, after all! Just don't tell anyone my little secret – I'm **SCARED** of the **DARK**....

WHAT'S IN MY BAG?

My favourite Ghostier bandage. Gotta look my beast!

"You can't keep royalty under wraps"

BE A HOPELESS ROMANTIC

Draculaura™

Have you ever heard of a **VEGETARIAN VAMPIRE?** Well, that's me – I faint at the sight of blood! My dad Dracula wishes I'd **SINK MY FANGS** into a raw steak, but I'd rather make do with the veggie offerings in the Creepateria! I couldn't live my **CLAWSOME UNLIFE** without my beast ghoulfriends Frankie Stein and Clawdeen Wolf. Plus, of course, I've got **GORE-GEOUS** Clawd Wolf on **SPEED-DIAL** on my iCoffin! He's so **SCREAMY.**

"I'm a total sucker for a monster who wants to sweep me off my feet"

GE-OGRE-PHY!

I'm so over ge-ogre-phy. It's totally yawnsome once you've been around the world and back again for 1599 years! But that doesn't mean you shouldn't be paying attention — if you're a newbie, ge-ogre-phy can be a clawsome class.

Spring break

Too much school, not enough howliday? Imagine you're on spring break with your ghouls and write a postcard home about the freaky-fab sights you've seen.

Dear.........................

Ghouls rule! Monster love

.... XXX

Address:

....

....

....

....

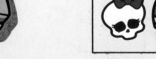

The ghouls come from scary-cool places all over the world and they're super proud of their scare-itages. Can you work out which ghoul comes from where? Write the correct names under the pictures.

Abbey Bominable

Rochelle Goyle

Skelita Calaveras™

Draculaura

Honey Swamp™

Nefera de Nile™

The Himalayas:..

Transylvania:..

New Goreleans:..

Scaris:..

Hexico:..

Ancient Egypt:..

Answers on **PAGE 69**

13

MONSTER HIGH

HOME ICK BAKE SALE!

Ms Kindergrübber here with my best students, who have created some scary recipes! I did have to promise Deuce that I wouldn't tell anyone he's such a good cook – apparently it could hurt his stone-cold school cred!

GET A GROAN-UP TO HELP YOU WITH YOUR BAKES!

Deuce Gorgon's

Monster Brownies

Hey, dudes – get ready to rock out with my freaktacular brownies!

1 Get an adult to preheat the oven to 180°C/350°F/Gas 4. Grease a 20 cm square baking tray.

2 Beat together the melted butter and caster sugar, then add the eggs and mix well. In a separate bowl, combine the flour, cocoa and salt. Stir into the sugar mixture. Mix in the vanilla extract and spread evenly into your prepared tin.

3 Bake the brownies for 25 to 30 minutes in the preheated oven or until the edges are firm. Leave to cool, then ask an adult to cut it into squares.

4 Use one of our freaky-fab templates to make a stencil on card. Place carefully on a brownie and dust over icing sugar. Instant monster style!

INGREDIENTS

125 g unsalted butter, melted

200 g caster sugar

2 eggs

75 g self-raising flour

25 g unsweetened cocoa powder

Pinch of salt

1 tsp vanilla extract

Icing sugar, to dust

Templates

14

Draculaura's
Scary Smoothie

Wash down these creeperific bakes with my gore-geous green shake! It's perfect for a vampire veggie like me.

INGREDIENTS
2 kiwis, peeled
Quarter of 1 lime, peeled
1 banana, peeled
Mint leaves, to taste
250 ml apple juice

Get an adult to help you put all the ingredients in a blender. Then blitz until you have a whole load of totally feel-good scarylicious smoothie! Now all that's left to do is drink up. Killer!

TRY EXPERIMENTING WITH OTHER FRUITS LIKE STRAWBERRIES, PEACHES AND PEARS - OR YOU COULD EVEN ADD A HANDFUL OF SPINACH LEAVES TO MAKE YOUR SMOOTHIE SUPER-HEALTHY!

Wydowna Spider's™
Cobweb Icing

1 Ask an adult to help you mix the icing sugar with a little hot water so you have a smooth, spreadable icing. Use two-thirds of the mixture to cover the tops of the ready-made cupcakes, smoothing with the back of a spoon.

2 Mix the remaining icing with the cocoa powder until smooth. Spoon into a piping bag with a small hole cut at the end. Pipe two or three circles, evenly spaced apart, onto the tops of the cupcakes.

3 Take a toothpick and use it to gently drag the icing to create a spider's web design. It's easy for me with my six arms, but do ask an adult to help if it's a bit tricky! Now stand back and admire your scary-cool skills!

INGREDIENTS
6 plain ready-made cupcakes
125 g icing sugar
Hot water
1 tsp cocoa powder

YOU COULD USE A DARK ICING PEN INSTEAD OF THE COCOA ICING IF YOU PREFER

15

SKULLASTICS

CLAWCULUS

I may be very intelligent yeti, though not yet in the English speaking. But in the maths, I am cool. Still doesn't mean I don't need little bit help from my friends. Let's do their number puzzles together!

Cleo's pyramids

Cleo de Nile is Monster High's star pupil at geometry. Here she puts you to the test. Add up the two squares next to each other and write the sum in the box above until you reach the tops of the pyramids.

4   5   10   1

16   12   8

5

GEOMETRY
Ancient Egyptian princess Cleo thinks anything that involves triangles and pyramids is as easy as pie ... or should that be pi?

Ghoulia's secret code

Ghoulia may be the biggest ogre-achiever when it comes to skullastics but she's not so hot at telling other monsters how she feels. Can you crack her computer code and read her secret message to Slo Mo?

ZOMBIE CRUSH

Zombie lovebirds Ghoulia and Slo Mo are both proud to be nerds and share a love of numbers. They're not so keen on subjects that involve talking.

2 5

13 25

26 15 13 2 9 5

___ ___ ___

___ ___ ___ ___

A	1	N	14
B	2	O	15
C	3	P	16
D	4	Q	17
E	5	R	18
F	6	S	19
G	7	T	20
H	8	U	21
I	9	V	22
J	10	W	23
K	11	X	24
L	12	Y	25
M	13	Z	26

Slo Mo's sudokus

Slo Mo thinks that advanced clawculus is amazingly interesting even when it's devilishly difficult. How about you? Can you crack his spooktacular sudokus? Fill in the grids with the numbers from 1 to 4 so that each number appears just once in each row, column and block.

Grid 1:
- Row 2: 2 (left), 4 (right)
- Row 3: 3
- Row 4: 1

Grid 2:
- Row 1: 1
- Row 2: 4
- Row 3: 2
- Row 4: 3

It's time for one of Mr Hackington's Scary Aptitude Tests! Put your Monster High knowledge to the test and see how you score. Get quizzing!

1 Which two students were made in a laboratory?

a) Holt Hyde and Jackson Jekyll .... ☐
b) Frankie Stein and Robecca Steam ..... ☐
c) Draculaura and Cleo de Nile .... ☐

2 How long was Johnny Spirit in detention for?

a) 3 hours .... ☐
b) 30 days .... ☐
c) 3000 years .... ☐

3 Why do Gillington 'Gil' Webber's parents disapprove of Lagoona Blue?

a) Because she's a sea monster .... ☐
b) Because she's flunking school .... ☐
c) Because she has a piranha as a pet .. ☐

4 What is Abbey Bominable's native language?

a) Zombie .... ☐
b) Vampire .... ☐
c) Yetish .... ☐

5 How did Cleo break Ghoulia's glasses?

a) She trod on them .... ☐
b) She cracked the lenses by screaming ☐
c) She let her snake Hissette™ eat them ☐

6 Which students joined Nefera's Fear Squad after she sacked the ghouls?

a) Toralei, Meowlody and Purrsephone.. ☐
b) Operetta, Rochelle and Robecca ...... ☐
c) Deuce, Manny and Neighthan .... ☐

QUIZ RULES
It's simple! Just tick your chosen answers then check them on page 69. For every correct answer you score 1 point. Why not quiz your mates too?

12 What is the name of Headmistress Bloodgood's horse?

a) Shiver .... ☐
b) Captain Penny ...... ☐
c) Nightmare .... ☐

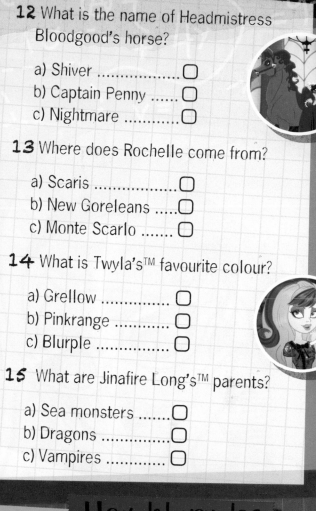

13 Where does Rochelle come from?

a) Scaris .... ☐
b) New Goreleans ..... ☐
c) Monte Scarlo .... ☐

14 What is Twyla's™ favourite colour?

a) Grellow .... ☐
b) Pinkrange .... ☐
c) Blurple .... ☐

15 What are Jinafire Long's™ parents?

a) Sea monsters .... ☐
b) Dragons .... ☐
c) Vampires .... ☐

7 What's the name of the fearleading legend who helped the Fear Squad to victory at Monster Mashionals?

a) Count Dracula .... ☐
b) Scary Murphy .... ☐
c) Moanatella Ghostier .... ☐

8 Who does Holt Hyde have a crush on?

a) Venus McFlytrap .... ☐
b) Draculaura .... ☐
c) Frankie Stein .... ☐

9 Roughly how old is Draculaura?

a) 16 days old .... ☐
b) 16 years old .... ☐
c) 1600 years old .... ☐

10 What is Clawdeen Wolf's favourite food?

a) Carrot sticks .... ☐
b) Fairy cakes .... ☐
c) Rare steak .... ☐

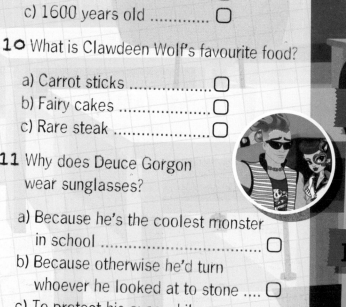

11 Why does Deuce Gorgon wear sunglasses?

a) Because he's the coolest monster in school .... ☐
b) Because otherwise he'd turn whoever he looked at to stone .... ☐
c) To protect his eyes while he's cooking .... ☐

How did you do?

MORE THAN 10

Top of the class
Freaky-fab! You're a total expert on all things Monster High – are you sure you're not a student there?

FROM 5 TO 10

Could do better
You know quite a bit about the wacky world of Monster High but there are a few gaps in your knowledge. Get studying!

LESS THAN 5

Voltageous fail!
Have you been hiding in the catacombs, ghoulfriend? You need the beginner's class on Monster High and quick!

Answers on PAGE 69

MONSTER HIGH

BE A SKULLASTIC SMARTIE

Ghoulia Yelps™

URRRGGGH! Translation: You won't see me without my 'GEEK-CHIC' glasses – after all, I am legally dead in both eyes, being a ZOMBIE. But I'd rather broaden my MIND than follow FREAKY fashion. I love every single subject on the SLIME-TABLE. I also use my SCARY SMARTS to help my GFFs, like when I fixed FRANKIE'S GPS so she could find her way around. My one FLAW is that I only speak ZOMBIE.

"You can't hurry genius"

ACHIEVE PEACE ON EARTH

(AND IN THE SEA)

Lagoona Blue™

I'm the daughter of the Sea Monster so I'm all about the **OCEAN**. Just check out my **SEA-SATIONAL** blue skin, **SURFER-GIRL CURLS** and **FINTASTIC FINS**! But you don't have to be an aqua-some **SEA CREATURE** to be my GFF – I'll **FANG OUT** with any ghoul, as long as they don't treat the **OCEAN** like their own personal rubbish bin! I've even crossed the **SALT-WATER DIVIDE** for my gore-geous m manster **GIL WEBBER**™ – but the **TIDE OF TRUE LOVE** never flows smoothly....

"I try to be at peace with my fellow monsters"

WHAT'S IN MY BAG?

Gallons of monsturizer – my skin gets so dry out of the water!

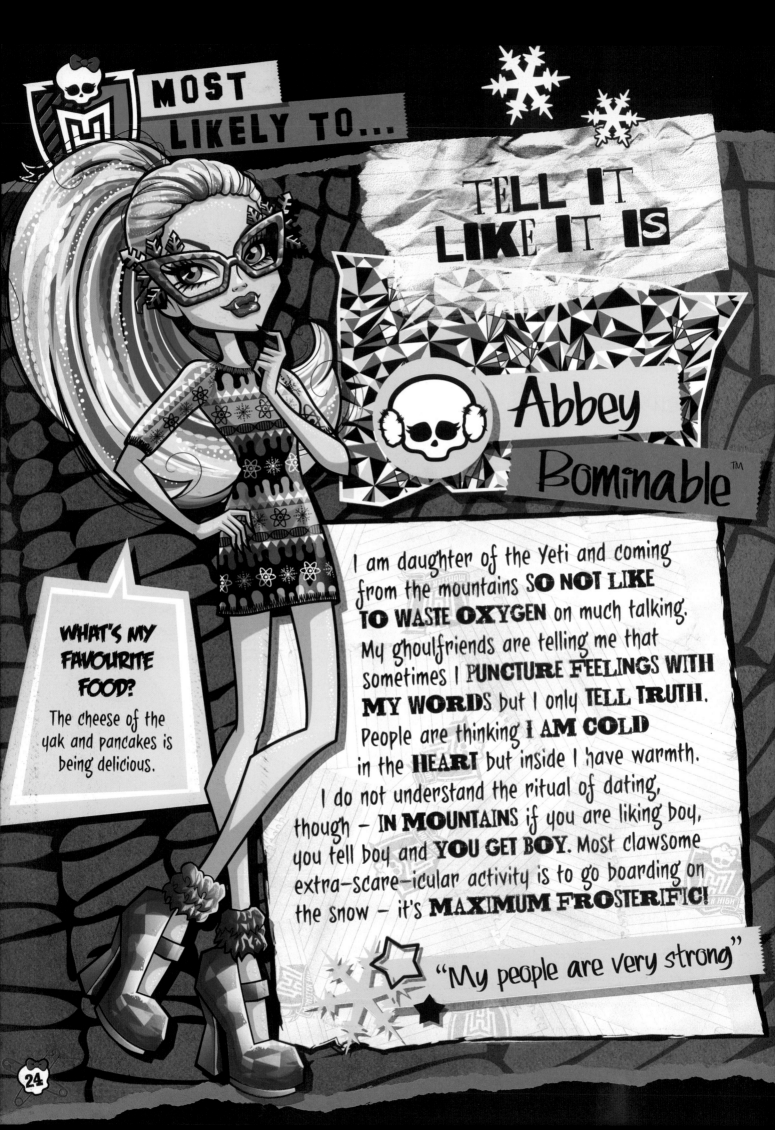

TELL IT LIKE IT IS

Abbey Bominable™

WHAT'S MY FAVOURITE FOOD?

The cheese of the yak and pancakes is being delicious.

I am daughter of the Yeti and coming from the mountains **SO NOT LIKE TO WASTE OXYGEN** on much talking. My ghoulfriends are telling me that sometimes I **PUNCTURE FEELINGS WITH MY WORDS** but I only **TELL TRUTH**. People are thinking **I AM COLD** in the **HEART** but inside I have warmth. I do not understand the ritual of dating, though – **IN MOUNTAINS** if you are liking boy, you tell boy and **YOU GET BOY**. Most clawsome extra-scare-icular activity is to go boarding on the snow – it's **MAXIMUM FROSTERIFIC!**

"My people are very strong"

24

LET YOU
HAVE ALL
THE NEWS

Spectra
Vondergeist™

Contrary to **SOME RUMOUR**S – I'm a
JOURNALIST. It's up to me to find out all the
behind-the-screams **COMINGS AND**
GROANINGS and print it in **THE**
GHOST POST. When I'm floating down
the **COFFIN CORRIDOR**s in my
GORE-GEOUS silk-and-metal outfits,
I keep my eyes and ears open for all
the **LATEST NEWS**. I don't have GFFs
as friendships might compromise my **JOURNALISTIC**
INTEGRITY. It's a sacrifice I make for my art....

"It can be very difficult being
the only one in the know"

COMIC BOOK CLUB

Ghoulia Yelps here – number-one comic book fan! Remember when I became superhero Ms Deadfast? Write captions for the pictures below to bring the scene to unlife. I've filled in a couple to help you get started!

The priceless issue 0 of *Deadfast* – the rarest comic book known to man or monster – is kept safely behind glass.

Ms Deadfast springs into action, using her super speed to avoid the villain's attacks – and ties him up with rope!

MONSTER HIGH

Draculaur

FEARLEADING FUN!

My Fear Squad is the beast thing to ever happen to Monster High. In case you've been in a coffin for the last thousand years, we just won at Monster Mashionals. It's thanks to me – I am Cleo de Nile, after all.

My ghouls are pretty fiercesome at fearleading, but they could all improve. Read my reports, then write the name under the description that matches!

Frankie Stein

A
This fur-rocious fearleader needs to learn she's not the centre of attention – that place is reserved exclusively for me!

B
Lots of room for improvement here! Must, repeat must, stop shuffling, moaning and groaning. It's quite off-putting for the rest of us.

C

I demand total focus during fearleading practice and this lovestruck member is all too often distracted by thoughts of her favourite manster.

Clawdeen Wolf

Ghoulia Yelps

D

She's got heaps of school spirit and is a monster mover – impressive for one so young! The whole limbs flying off thing is getting pretty tired, though....

Count 'em up!

Oh my Ra! There are a few too many pompoms in our fearleading rehearsal and they're getting in the way of our freaky-fab moves. Count them up and put your answer in the box to the right.

How many?

Answers on PAGE 69

29

MONSTER MUSIC CLUB

Howdy, music fans – it's undead rocker Operetta™ here! Step into the creepy catacombs and come inside my recording studio for a seriously monsterific jam session.

The Monster High song is scary cool, right? Well, you can make it even more freaktacular by adding your own verse. Just in case you need help, here are my tips for writing song lyrics!

- Write about your interests, favourite ghouls or subjects
- Keep your lyrics short and sweet so they pack a punch!
- Think about rhyming words, like 'ghost'/'most' or 'scream'/'dream'
- Sing your lyrics aloud and listen to how they sound
- Get together with your ghoulfriends – each write your own verse, then perform in front of your adoring fans!

Tangled web

a

b

c

Answer

Which path will lead Memphis 'Daddy O' Longlegs™, my pet spider, to me? Write it in the answer box!

Stage fright!

Hi ghouls, I'm Casta Fierce™ and I'd love to sing the Monster High song – but if I get the lyrics wrong I risk turning my audience into ... well ... frogs. Help me avoid disaster and fill in the gaps with the right monsters' names.

Cleo de Nile

Ms Lagoon

Draculaura

Who goes where?

Clawdeen Wolf

Frankie

Deuce

_ _ _ _ _ _ _ _ _ 's
GOT ME FALLIN' APART

_ _ _ _ _ _ _ _ _ _ _ _ 's
STEALIN' MY HEART

_ _ _ _ _ _ _ _ _ _ _ _ ,
**YOU MAKE ME HOWL
AT THE MOON**

_ _ _ _ _ _ _ _ , YOU'RE THE
FINEST FISH IN THIS LAGOON

_ _ _ _ _ _ _ _ _ _ _ ,
YOU SO BEGUILE
**EVEN THOUGH YOU
ACT SO VILE**

AND _ _ _ _ _ _ **HAS
STONE-COLD STYLE**

Answers on PAGE 69

33

SWIM CLUB

Welcome to Swim Club, ghoulfriends! My name is Lagoona Blue and I love splashing about in the water, whether it's at Gloom Beach or in the school pool!

Under water

Three students have fallen into the pool – talk about mortalfying! Work out who the underwater monsters are and write their names in the boxes below.

Three of my gore-geous ghoulfriends have got changed for Swim Club in such a rush that they're all mixed up. Can you figure out which swimsuit and shoes belong to which ghoul so they can hit the water? Put the answers in the 'Work it out' boxes below!

A
B
C

1
2
3

Swim sudoku

Are you ready for some water-themed puzzle fun? Fill in my missing aqua-some symbols so that all four of them appear just once in each row, column and box of four squares. G'luck!

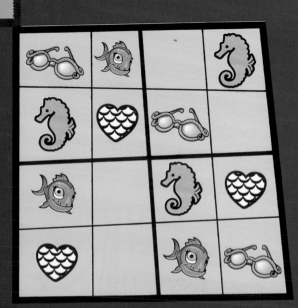

Work it out!

___ ___ ___

___ ___ ___

Answers on PAGE 69

35

PHYSICAL DEAD-UCATION

As the son of the Minotaur, Manny Taur knows all about mazes – he was even born in a labyrinth! Can you find your way out from the centre of Manny's fiendish maze?

Start

Way out

Monster pep rally

Can you spot 10 **DIFFERENCES** between these pics of Manny and the ghouls rallying the fans at the game? Circle the differences on picture B.

Count the balls!

Help Manny count up his footballs, then write your answer on the notepaper!

How many?

Answers on **PAGE 69**

37

FASHIONABLY FIERCE!

Hey fashionistas – Sirena Von Boo here! I know killer style is a big deal at Monster High, but you don't need the latest thing from the Maul to look totally ghoul. It's way more phantastic if you bling up items of clothing or axe-cessories that are just floating about in your scare-drobe. Check out mine and Operetta's top tips for dead chic new looks....

Operetta's turn-ups

Don't be a wallflower! Y'all get noticed with this quick-and-easy rockabilly update on your fave ol' denims.

1 Fold up the bottoms of your jeans to the depth you want. Measure the height and width of the turn-ups, adding 1 cm to each. Make card templates for the front and back.

YOU WILL NEED
Ruler
Card and pencil
Scissors
1 m of washable patterned fabric (I love garish tartan but go for whatever you like beast!)
Fabric glue
Pair of jeans
Pins

2 Draw round the templates onto the back of the patterned fabric, then cut the shapes out.

3 Fold over 1 cm of fabric all around the edge of each piece. Glue the folded edges in place to give a clean edge.

4 Turn your jeans inside-out. Place the fabric panels on the bottom of the jeans and pin in place.

5 Removing the pins one by one as you go, carefully glue the fabric panels onto the jeans.

6 Once the glue has dried, turn the jeans the right way out and fold over your creeperific turn-ups! Now rock that rockabilly lurk!

Hey! Don't grab an ordinary old plastic bag every time you float to the Maul – design your own tote bag instead. First get a plain tote, then sketch on a design of your choice. Check out my freaky-fab ideas below – and colour in with fabric paint. For extra bling, add strings of pearls, chains, sequins and glitter!

Ideas

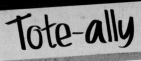

So, what's your bag?

Logo loco! Show your school spirit by copying the Monster High badge, complete with skull and bow, onto your bag. Practise on scrap paper first to make sure you get it right.

If you're a treasure hunter like me, you'll want to give your tote a vintage makeover and cover it with ghoul jewels like my signature pearls and jangly chains.

Choose a design that reflects your personality. If you're a romantic like Draculaura, go for hearts and roses, while sea-lovers like Lagoona Blue might choose something ocean-inspired and frosty types like Abbey Bominable could opt for snowflakes. Cool!

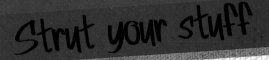

Strut your stuff

Why not stage a fierce fashion show with your ghoulfriends? Pull on your scary-cool denim turn-ups and sling your customized tote over your shoulder – or come up with your own freaky-fab ideas – then turn your bedroom into a catwalk. Take turns to prowl up and down while the rest of your ghoulfriends scream their approval!

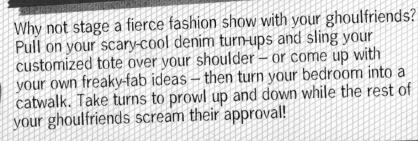

EXTRA-SCARE-ICULAR

POSTER PANIC

The fashionistas are ready to strut the werecatwalk at this year's Fierce Fashion Show. But there's one problem.... The school printer's broken and the posters aren't ready. Get busy drawing so the ghouls can line the coffin corridor with posters for the show!

2016 FASHION SHOW

TO DRAW YOUR SPOOKTACULAR POSTER, COPY
EACH SQUARE INTO THE BLANK GRID ON THIS
PAGE, THEN COLOUR IT IN

BRING-YOUR-PET-TO-SCHOOL DAY

I'm Headmistress Bloodgood and I've invited the ghouls to bring their furry (or spiky or slimy) friends to school. The coffin corridors are even more creature-crazy than usual!

Pet puzzler

Find the pets' names in this wordsearch. Remember, they can go diagonally as well as up, down and sideways!

```
S R E D A M E M P H I S C
A H I S S E T T E A O W A
C B A L W S H I V E R E P
A I C O N A S R T I L E T
S I R H O O T S A L O T A
  E A L Z A Y C F I
  W Y B I N U A N
  O L A J T S N P
  R T I D A H G E
  E O V M A G I S N
  W U T U T N O A N
  A X R I C A N A Y
```

ROUX™
CAPTAIN PENNY™
CHEWLIAN™
MEMPHIS™
CUSHION™
SWEET FANGS™
WATZIT™
SIR HOOTS A LOT™
SHIVER™
HISSETTE™

Answers on **PAGE 69**

Animal magic!

The pets have started rampaging through the school! Only three of the ghouls have a clear path to their creature – can you work out which ones? If so, place a tick by their names!

MONSTER MASH

Frankie's pet Watzit was made from stitched-together body parts. He barks like a dog and purrs like a cat!

Howleen Wolf

Venus McFlytrap

Toralei Stripe

Robecca Steam

Rochelle Goyle

Cushion

Roux

Sweet Fangs

Captain Penny

Chewlian

ROCK ON!

Operetta says Memphis 'Daddy O' Longlegs is unlike any other spider – "Unless you've seen one rocking a pompadour while playing a stand-up bass!"

In the shadows?

A   B   C

Can you recognize the purr-fect pets of Monster High just by their scary-cool silhouettes? Write the correct name under each.

45

MONSTER HIGH

WALK UNDER A LADDER

Catty Noir™

I'm **CREEPERIFICALLY SUPERSTITIOUS**! Before I go on stage I have a ritual of eating **13** items of food and I **WEAR** a piece of broken mirror. Being a **WERECAT POP STAR** was pretty **CLAWSOME**, but it's totally ghoul to be at **MONSTER HIGH**, making GFFs and learning tons of stuff. I'm having **THE TIME OF MY UNLIFE!**

13

"After years of having every minute of my unlife planned for me, I am OH-VER IT!"

MONSTER HIGH

BE AN ECO-WARRIOR

Venus McFlytrap™

I think protecting the ENVIRONMENT is SCARY COOL. After all, I'm the daughter of the PLANT MONSTER and get my nourishment from the AIR and SOIL – so it's only NATURAL that I want them to be as CLEAN as possible. My ghoulfriends are SPOOKTACULARLY SUPPORTIVE of the cause – although I do sometimes have to use my POLLENS OF PERSUASION to get other MONSTERS on my side. Now find me a TREE TO HUG!

FAVE SUBJECT?
Biteology. I wanna find out all about the plants and trees!

"Be bright, be bold, be involved!"

47

MONSTER HIGH

TAKE A TUMBLE

Iris Clops™

OOPS! Hey, who put those stairs there? I guess you could **CALL ME CLUMSY** – just take a look at my **BUMPS AND BRUISES!** I like to say it's down to my lack of **DEPTH PERCEPTION** on account of being a cyclops. But maybe my ghoulfriends are right and **I DON'T ALWAYS LOOK** where I'm going.... My fave thing? **FANGING OUT** and **STARING AT THE STARS** with my gore-geous **MANSTER** Manny Taur™. **TOAD-ALLY DEFRIGHTFUL.**

"It's just so clawsome to look up into the night sky and wonder who or what is out there."

WHAT'S IN MY BAG?

Custom-made sunglasses for my one eye.

PHOTO BOMB A PICTURE

Lorna McNessie™

I never met a **PHOTO** I didna want tae be a part of and if there's a chance tae do some **PHOTO BOMBING** I'm goin' tae take it! My parents don't approve, of course, being notoriously camera-shy **LOCH NESS MONSTER**s. But I am loyal to **MY CLAN** when it comes to expressing my **KILLER STYLE**. Being a ghoul from the **HIGHLANDS** I wear my **TARTAN KNITS AND KILTS** with **PRIDE**.

"It's nae like I want tae ruin a shot, but it's so much fun!

49

MONSTER PROM

MONSTER HIGH

PARTY TIME!

I am Cleo de Nile and I'm quite literally a party queen — so, of course, I'm in charge of planning a creeperific prom party. Put on your killer clothes and dancing shoes and have the time of your unlife!

Skull-tastic hairband

Really look the undead part at the prom with this scary-cool hair axe-cessory...

Get an adult to help you with the stitching!

1 Place your Monster High skull and bow template onto white felt and draw round it. Repeat to make two skull and bow felt shapes, then cut them both out.

2 Glue the shapes together. Use your black fabric pen to draw the eyes, nose and the outline and details of the bow onto one side. Colour the bow in using your pink fabric pen.

3 Cut a length of elastic to fit round your head. Glue your felt skull and bow to the end of the elastic, then make a small stitch to secure. Now make your GFFs scream with delight at your new lurk!

Template

YOU WILL NEED
Skull and bow template
White felt
Pencil
Scissors
Fabric glue
Black and pink fabric pens
Elastic
Needle and thread

Scare-aoke scramble!

Make like songstress Catty Noir and test your vocal talents. It's the purr-fect way to get in the party mood!

Start by glamming yourselves up in your most freaky-fab clothes! Scare-dos and make-up complete the look.

Clear an area to be the stage and set up chairs for the 'judges'. Make scorecards from one to five. Take it in turns to perform, then tot up the scores to find the winner!

Totally nailed it

YOU WILL NEED:
Your best ghoulfriends
A quiet spot
Hand cream
Nail files
Nail varnish
of your
choice

If you're anything like me – but less royal, of course – you'll want your nails to look freaky-fab at your prom. Even Clawdeen's talons scrub up okay!

Wash your hands so they're eek-y clean, then monsturize with hand scream and file your claws neatly. For a school-friendly look, just paint on clear nail varnish – or try one of my scary-cool ideas ... if you dare:

- Plain black nails always look spooky, but add a coat of shimmer so they catch the undead eye
- Try neon green or yellow for a terribly toxic effect
- Paint your nails dark red, with a few drops coming down your fingers. Creeptastic!
- Try a classic gold polish. It looks really regal!

51

SPOOKTACULAR SELFIES

LAGOONA AND ROCHELLE: GHOULFRIENDS FOREVER!

AMANITA NIGHTSHADE SNAPS A SOLO SELFIE!

52

VENUS MCFLYTRAP HAS FIERCE FLOWER POWER!

Prom King & Queen

THE GHOULS ARE STRUTTING THEIR SCARY-COOL STUFF!

PRE-PROM FAMILY SNAP!

53

MONSTER HIGH

TURD UP LATE

Robecca Steam™

I'm afraid I **CAN'T TALK** for long – I seem to be **RUNNING LATE** for my next **LESSON**. Ever since my accident on the **SKULTIMATE ROLLER MAZE** 100 years ago, there appears to be a problem with **MY TIME-KEEPING MECHANISM!**

I think of myself as an **OLD-FASHIONED** sort of **ROBOT** but my GFFS assure me that my look is something called '**STEAM PUNK**', which is apparently quite the **LATEST THING!**

"My new friends have been very accepting and scary sweet"

E A ROCK-

MOST LIKELY TO...

BE A ROCK-SOLID FRIEND

Rochelle Goyle™

MONSTER HIGH is – how you say? – a **STEPPING STONE** to an unlife beyond the rooftops. Back home in **SCARIS**, France, all my friends were made of stone, but here I have met **MONSTER**s of every kind. Like all **GARGOYLES**, I am very protective of my ghoulfriends. But when I am not guarding **MY BEAST FRIENDS**, I am the **CREME-DE-LA-CREME** on the Skultimate Roller Maze.

"Travel beyond the stone you sit on"

WHAT'S IN MY LOCKER?
Roses. They have a certain je-ne-sais-quoi, non?

START A CATFIGHT

Toralei Stripe™

I guess my **FAVOURITE SUBJECT** is causing mischief. It's a **PURR-FECT** way to spend my days – when I'm not having a **WERECAT-NAP**, that is. And because I'm so **CLAWSOME** at mimicking voices, I'm **GRRREAT** at messing with **MONSTERS'** heads. Me and my **BEAST** feline friends Meowlody™ and Purrsephone™ love **PROWLING** the **COFFIN CORRIDORS** in our **FUR-ROCIOUSLY** cool outfits. It's a **SCREAM!**

"Oh no, did I do that?"

Deuce Gorgon – Son of Medusa

Clawd Wolf™ – Son of the Werewolf

Holt Hyde™ – Son of Mr and Mrs Hyde

THE MANSTERS

MEET THE SWOONSOME GUYS OF MONSTER HIGH...

Jackson Jekyll™ – Son of Dr and Mrs Jekyll

Gillington 'Gil' Webber – Son of the River Monster

Heath Burns™ – Son of a Fire Elemental

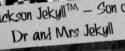

Sloman 'Slo Mo' Mortavitch™ – Son of the Zombies

Manny Taur – Son of the Minotaur

Invisi Billy™ – Son of the Invisible Man

FIND YOUR BEAST MONSTER MATE!

Imagine you're a Monster High newbie like Catty Noir — which ghoul would be your GFF? Find out here!

Would you rather go to a killer party than chill at home?

Is freaky-fab fashion your obsession?

NO

TOTALLY

NOT REALLY

YES

Would you be happy to fang out with anyone?

NOT REALLY

Do you have tons of school spirit?

YEP

NO WAY!

YEAH

NO WAY!

LAGOONA BLUE

Together, you and Lagoona could bring peace to Monster High. You're caring, friendly and will fang out with anyone at school.

CLEO DE NILE

You're an easy-going sort of ghoul, so you can handle Queen Cleo's regal rages! You know that beneath that designer-bandaged exterior beats a heart of gold.

FRANKIE STEIN

Like Frankie, you're more sweet than scary. The pair of you have so much positivity that together you would be truly electrifying!

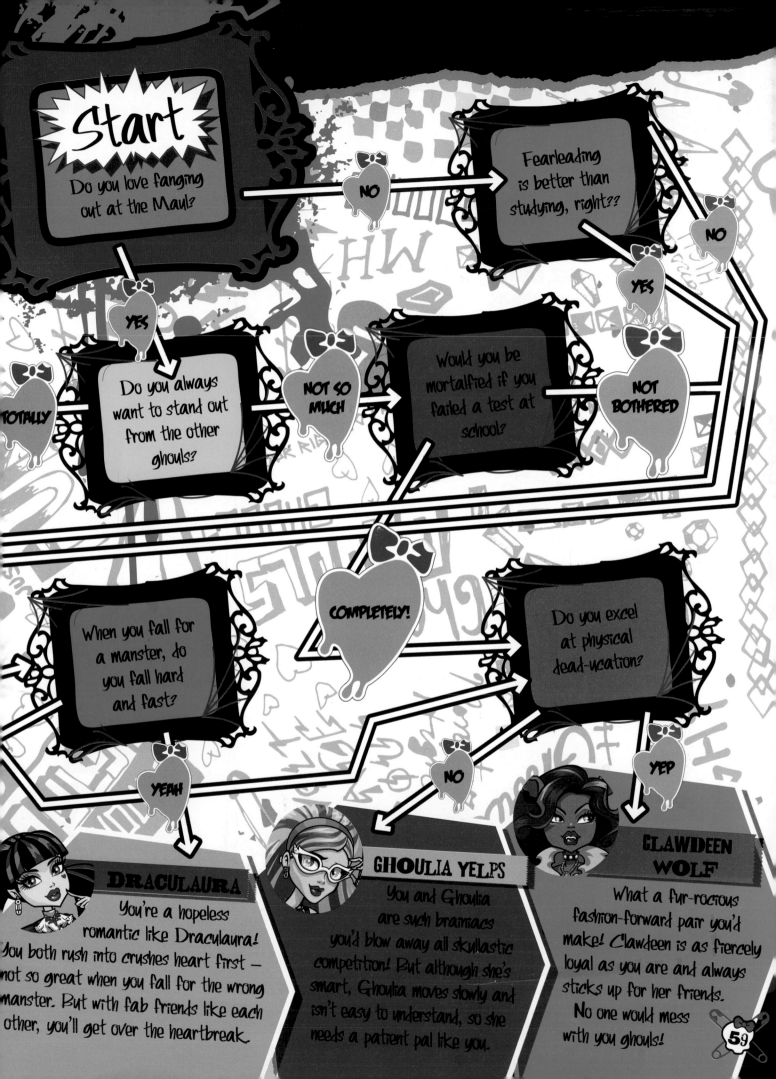

Start
Do you love fanging out at the Maul?

NO

Fearleading is better than studying, right??

NO

YES

YES

Do you always want to stand out from the other ghouls?

NOT SO MUCH

Would you be mortalfied if you failed a test at school?

NOT BOTHERED

TOTALLY

When you fall for a manster, do you fall hard and fast?

COMPLETELY!

Do you excel at physical dead-ucation?

YEAH

NO

YEP

DRACULAURA
You're a hopeless romantic like Draculaura! You both rush into crushes heart first — not so great when you fall for the wrong manster. But with fab friends like each other, you'll get over the heartbreak

GHOULIA YELPS
You and Ghoulia are such brainiacs you'd blow away all skullastic competition! But although she's smart, Ghoulia moves slowly and isn't easy to understand, so she needs a patient pal like you.

CLAWDEEN WOLF
What a fur-rocious fashion-forward pair you'd make! Clawdeen is as fiercely loyal as you are and always sticks up for her friends. No one would mess with you ghouls!

59

Farewell, fans!

POP STAR CATTY NOIR JUST WANTS TO BE A NORMAL GHOUL....

We love you!!!!

We want more!

JUST ONE OF THE GHOULS

Catty Noir leaves the fangtastic world of glamour and fame behind her ...

... to become just another ghoul at Monster High. She hopes the student bodies will accept her!

Now I'm going to take a break from showbiz!

As she steps out of her limo, though, she is greeted by fans — and when she prowls down the coffin corridors she's mobbed by the ghouls!

CATTY!!

We're so excited to have you here!

We love you, Catty!

WE ARE

MONSTERS!!!

GHOULFRIENDS FOREVER

THE GHOST POST

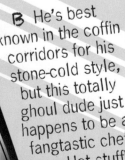

Hey there, ghoulfriends — it's Spectra V here with all the latest behind-the-screams info from the coffin corridors! This year, I've been more vigilant than ever digging up scary-cool stories for you to enjoy. So what if I don't get every fact right all the time?

Roarsome rumours

Unlife would be pretty boring without a few juicy rumours, right? The only problem is, I've forgotten who my stories are about! Read each text message and see if you can tell which of the monsters below I've been writing about, then put your answers in the box.
Good luck, ghouls!

Venus McFlytrap

Cleo de Nile

Lagoona Blue

Deuce Gorgon

A This fearleading princess can be utterly terrifying. But did you know that she has a secret — she's scared of the dark. Mortalfying!

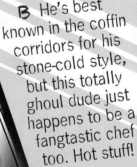

B He's best known in the coffin corridors for his stone-cold style, but this totally ghoul dude just happens to be a fangtastic chef too. Hot stuff!

My diary is packed with spooky secrets and terrifying tales. It would be a catastrophe if it fell into the wrong monster's hands, so I write my entries in code. Can you crack the code and reveal what I've written? Each symbol stands for a different letter – work out which is which and you'll be able to read my words!

AGONY AUNT
I'm known for my sensitivity and tact – just take a look at my problems page Oh My Oracle in the school paper. Journo-tastic!

January 21st

Whe🦇 I s🕸w 🔷he he🕸dli🦇e "🔷he Re🕸l V🕸🦇dergeis🔷s" I c🔷uld🦇'🔷 believe my eyes! Gh🕸uli🕸 h🕸d u🦇c🕸vered 🔷he 🔷r🕸gic his🔷🕸ry 🕸f my f🕸mily. She's pr🕸mised 🔷o keep my secre🔷, s🕸 🦇🕸b🕸dy 🦇eed ever k🦇🕸w 🔷h🕸t we were r🕸y🕸l🔷y bu🔷 were exiled by my evil u🦇cle.

🕸 _____ 🦇 _____ 💀 _____ 🔷 _____

C She's a salt-water stunner but her love life isn't going swimmingly. That might be because her boo is a fresh-water freak. Star-crossed lovers!

D This eco-friendly ghoul comes across as a sweet little flower but she sometimes uses her 'pollens of persuasion' on monsters to get her own way!

Your answers

GHOULFRIENDS FOREVER

MONSTER HIGH

AUTOGRAPHS

No Monster High Fearbook would be complete without your ghoulfriends' signatures! You can tell a lot about a monster by their handwriting, so check out a few scribbles by the ghouls — then get your friends to add their own!

Ula D's letters slant to the right, meaning she's open and sociable

Draculaura

Clawdeen's spiky scrawl reflects her feisty personality

Clawdeen Wolf

Neat and old-fashioned, just like the ghoul herself!

Robecca Steam

Now get your ghoulfriends to sign their names — and see what you can learn about their personalities from their scribbles!

....

....

....

....

....

Slightly curly script like this signifies a sympathetic character

Venus McFlytrap

....

....

Using all capital letters suggests a straightforward kinda manster

....

SLO MO

....

ANSWERS

GE-OGRE-PHY!

Pages 12–13
The Himalayas – Abbey Bominable
Transylvania – Draculaura
New Goreleans – Honey Swamp
Scaris – Rochelle Goyle
Hexico – Skelita Calaveras
Ancient Egypt – Nefera de Nile

CLAWCULUS

Pages 18–19
Ghoulia's secret code:
BE MY ZOMBIE

S.A.T.S

Pages 20–21
1 = b, 2 = c, 3 = a, 4 = c, 5 = b, 6 = a,
7 = b, 8 = c, 9 = c, 10 = c, 11 = b,
12 = c, 13 = a, 14 = c, 15 = b

FEARLEADING FUN!

Pages 28–29
A = Clawdeen Wolf, B = Ghoulia Yelps,
C = Draculaura, D = Frankie Stein

There are 19 pompoms

MUSIC CLUB

Pages 32–33
Tangled web: b leads to Operetta

Stage fright: Frankie, Draculaura, Clawdeen
Wolf, Ms Lagoon, Cleo de Nile, Deuce

SWIM CLUB

Pages 34–35
Under water: A – Clawdeen,
B – Holt, C – Clawd

Monster mash:
Draculaura – C and 2,
Venus McFlytrap – A and 3,
Rochelle Goyle – B and 1

PHYSICAL DEAD-UCATION

Pages 36–37

Count the balls:
There are 25 footballs

PETS

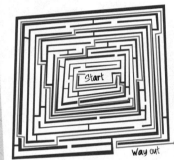

Pages 44–45
Animal magic!:
Howleen Wolf
Venus McFlytrap
Robecca Steam

In the shadows:
A – Sir Hoots A Lot,
B – Shiver, C – Hissette

THE GHOST POST

Pages 64–65
Roarsome rumours: A = Cleo de Nile, B = Deuce
Gorgon, C = Lagoona Blue, D = Venus McFlytrap

Die-ary decipher: ✳ A 🐍 N 💀 O 💎 T